Hans Jürgen Press

The Black Hand Gang
and the
Mysterious House

Illustrations by the author

Ravensburger Buchverlag

Als Ravensburger Taschenbuch
Band 52066
erschienen 1978
Erstmals in den Ravensburger
Taschenbüchern erschienen 1978
(als RTB 504)

Die Abenteuer der „schwarzen hand" wurden
unter der Mitarbeit von Fritz Raab im
STERNCHEN, der Kinderbeilage des STERN
Magazins, erstmals veröffentlicht.

Die deutsche Originalausgabe erschien 1965
im Otto Maier Verlag Ravensburg
© 1987 Ravensburger Buchverlag
Otto Maier GmbH

Die englische Erstausgabe erschien 1976
bei Methuen Children's Books Ltd., London
© 1976 by Methuen Children's Books Ltd.,
London für die englische Textfassung
Aus dem Deutschen von Barbara Littlewood
Bearbeitung: Uwe Lüer

Umschlagillustration: Hans Jürgen Press

Printed in Germany

12 13 14   14 13

ISBN 978-3-473-52066-4

www.ravensburger.de

Hans Jürgen Press

**The Black Hand Gang
and the Mysterious house**

Von Hans Jürgen Press
sind in den Ravensburger Taschenbüchern
außerdem erschienen:

RTB 52028
Die Abenteuer der „schwarzen Hand"

RTB 52067
The Black Hand Gang
and the Treasure in Breezy Lake

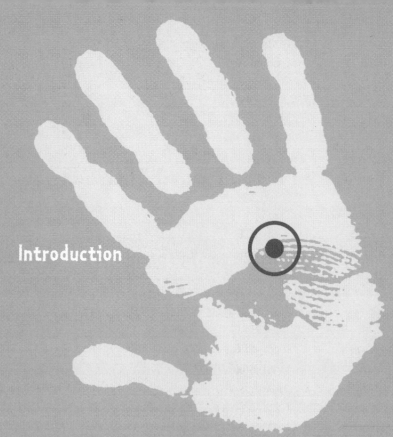

Introduction

to take a stroll	– einen Streifengang machen	inseparable	– unzertrennlich
to stare at	= to look at	squirrel	– Eichhörnchen
faded	– verblichen	locally	= in the place where they live
to pin to	– anheften an		
handprint	– Handabdruck	sleuth	= detective
sergeant	– Wachtmeister	to enable	– befähigen, in die Lage versetzen
to get up to some funny tricks	– lustige Einfälle haben		
		skill	– Geschicklichkeit
kids	= children	clue	– hier: Spur, Hinweis
gang	– Bande	trail	– Fährte
to track down	– zur Strecke bringen	to mark down	= to write down
		to check	– überprüfen, auswerten
creaking	– krächzend		
pigeon loft	– Taubenschlag	score	– Punktzahl Trefferzahl
leader	– Anführer		
quick-witted	– schlagfertig, aufgeweckt		

Police Sergeant Shorthouse was taking a stroll along Canal Street, when he paused for a moment in the doorway of Number 49 and stared at a faded notice pinned to the doorpost. It was a piece of paper with a black handprint. The sergeant shook his head and smiled.

"Children really do get up to some funny tricks these days," he murmured, half to himself. He was thinking of a group of kids who called themselves "The Black Hand Gang" and of the clever way that they had learned to track down criminals.

At the top of this house, up seventy-two creaking stairs, was their clubroom, called the "Airport", just under the pigeon loft on the roof. The Black Hand Gang met there regularly after school. Frank, who played the trumpet, was the leader; then there was quick-witted Angela; Ralph, who usually wore a striped sweater; and finally Keith W.S. and his inseparable companion, a squirrel. (W.S. stands for "With Squirrel".)

The Black Hand Gang's adventures had made them well known locally as amateur sleuths. This book tells how they began their successful career as detectives, and will enable you, the reader, to try your skill at discovering the clues.

⊙➜ You can follow the trail by looking carefully at the illustrations. When you have found the right answer, mark it down on a piece of paper, and check your score on the last page.

The Mysterious House

I | A Sure Sign

The Black Hand Gang had been sitting up in the Airport as quiet as mice for an hour while they did their homework. Ralph chewed his pen and gazed fixedly out of the grimy window. There was a sudden, sharp snap. Keith W.S. cracked a nut for his squirrel and spat the shell into an empty jam jar. Ralph frowned.

"Which spelling is correct: 'pane' or 'pain'?" he whispered.

"It depends whether you're looking through it or feeling it inside you," Angela replied, laughing.

"Looking through it, of course, a window-pane like that one there ... Hey, what's that? No, there can't be!" Ralph scrubbed at the dirt on the window.

"What can't there be?" asked Frank.

"Anyone living in that house over there," Ralph answered.

"It's been empty for three years."

They all crowded round the window.

"We all know that only a couple of rats live there," said Keith W.S. "Look, the doors and windows are all barred shut."

"Let me have a look," said Angela, pressing her nose to the pane. After a few seconds she said, "I think Ralph's right. There really is someone in the house."

>+⊙→ ( ) **How did she guess there was someone in the mysterious house?**

sure	– sicher	to spit spat, spat	– spucken
to chew	– kauen	to frown	– die Stirn runzeln
grimy	= dirty	pane	– Fensterscheibe
snap	– Knacken	pain	– Schmerz
to crack	– knacken	to scrub	– wischen, scheuern

2 | The Heel on the Wall

It was obvious to the Black Hand Gang that there was someone living in the house because the chimney was smoking.

They kept a constant watch, and five days later their patience was rewarded. While Angela was on guard one evening, she saw the figure of a man climbing over the wall near the place where the boats were moored on the canal.

Next day the Black Hand Gang met before school to inspect the wall thoroughly. "Look, there!" called Keith W.S. suddenly.

"I can't see anything," Frank said.

Keith W.S. took the squirrel from his shoulder and placed it on the wall. It scampered down a creeper and seized something round. "Look at that!" Ralph exclaimed. "It's the heel of someone's shoe."

"Listen, all of you," said Frank. "We must look for a man with a heel off his shoe."

They started looking on their way to school. Angela sauntered along, swinging her bag and her satchel. Suddenly she exclaimed out loud. "Hey, there he is! That's him."

Later that day she described him to the rest of the gang and said, "We'll recognize him by his trousers."

>→•→ ◯ **What sort of trousers was the man without a heel to his shoe wearing?**

heel	–Absatz	to moor	– festmachen
obvious	– klar, einleuchtend	thoroughly	– gründlich
to keep a constant watch	– ständig beobachten	to scamper	– hier: klettern
		creeper	– Kletterpflanze
patience	– Geduld	to saunter	– schlendern
to reward	– belohnen	to recognize	– (wieder) erkennen
to be on guard	– auf der Lauer sein		

13

3 | The Rathole

The Gang sat up in the Airport listening intently to Angela's report. "Well, now we know that the man without a heel wears check trousers," Frank said.

"But no one's seen his face yet," Ralph pointed out.

"We'll get a chance as soon as we see him go into that house. Each of us must cover an entrance."

"And the windows," added Angela.

"Of course," Frank agreed.

Three minutes later they were all at their posts. Frank was watching the front door; Ralph, the gate by the canal; Angela stood by the garden gate watching the side road through two holes she had cut in her newspaper, and Keith W. S., disguised as a garden gnome, stood like a statue half hidden in a bed of nettles. Not even a mouse could have come in the back way without his seeing it. Two hours dragged by, but no one came near the house. "Tailing a suspect is the most boring part of a detective's life," Ralph thought, yawning.

"Oh, showers of nuts," whispered Keith W. S. as the truth suddenly dawned on him. "He's been inside the house all the time. No wonder. There's a hidden trap door, beautifully camouflaged, too."

>+⊙→ ◯ **Where was the secret entrance?**

intently	– gespannt	to tail	– beschatten
check trousers	– karierte Hose	suspect	– verdächtige Person
to cover	– sichern, beobachten	truth	– Wahrheit
entrance	– Eingang	dawn	– dämmern
disguised	– verkleidet	trap door	– Falltür, Geheimtür
gnome	– Zwerg	to camouflage	– tarnen
nettles	– Nesseln		

4 | The Telegram

Keith W.S. had hardly seen the man's face when the trap door snapped shut. The Black Hand Gang ran over to the tulip bed. Ralph sniffed at a flower.

"Artificial!" he said.

"Lift up the trap door," said Angela, firmly. "I'm going in. I want to know where it leads."

"What if something happens to you?" asked Keith W.S.

Angela showed them her bag. "I brought Isobel 13 with me in case."

Isobel 13 was the best pigeon the Black Hand Gang owned.

Angela disappeared down the hole. She crawled quietly along the passage and came out through a small door into a dark room. She began to look round, but before she could see something unusual she heard a noise. Quickly she scribbled on a piece of paper: "Inside house. Going to hide in chest. Love, Angela." Then she sent Isobel 13 off up the chimney with it.

"Where on earth is Angela?" said Frank, looking at his watch. "She's been down there for eleven minutes. I hope she's all right."

Ralph said, "Let's go up to the pigeon loft and see if there's any message."

They ran off and climbed up to the loft. Frank said, "There's Isobel 13, back already."

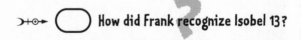 How did Frank recognize Isobel 13?

tulip	– Tulpe	to scribble	– kritzeln
artificial	– künstlich	chest	– Truhe
to crawl	– kriechen	message	– Botschaft

17

5 | Mr X's Study

When Frank had read out Angela's telegram, Ralph suggested
that they clean the soot off Isobel 13. Her flight up the chimney had made her black all over, but Frank said no.
"Let's just leave her. She'll clean herself."
Keith W. S. agreed: "Yes, she will. My squirrel always does."
"What do you suppose Angela's doing now?" asked Ralph.
Angela was still inside the mysterious house. Raising the lid of
the chest in which she had hidden, she peeped cautiously out.
Everything was quiet. Suddenly she noticed the door. A thin
ray of light shone through the keyhole. In a flash she was
across the room to the door and pressed her eye to the keyhole.
Mr X sat only a few feet away, his back to her, bent over
something on the table in front of him, examining it minutely.
A few minutes later the Airport door burst open. The Black
Hand Gang jumped up, shouting: "Thank goodness you're
safe, Angela."
"I'm all right!" she exclaimed. "I've found out what Mr X is
doing."

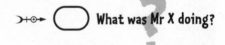 **What was Mr X doing?**

soot	– Ruß	cautiously	– vorsichtig
to raise	– anheben, hochheben	ray of light	– Lichtstrahl
		in a flash	– im Nu
to peep	– hervorgucken	minutely	– peinlich genau

6 | The Golden Cigar Band

"That's extraordinary," said Frank. "You're quite sure he was looking at postage stamps?"

"I saw him with my own eyes," Angela replied, "and I've brought you something else." She opened an old tin.

"Wherever did you find that old cigar stub?" cried Ralph in surprise.

"I picked it up in the secret passage," Angela said proudly.

The gang examined the stub. Frank remarked, "It must be a good brand, my father smokes cigars with a gold band only on very special occasions."

"But does he smoke Don Carlos?" asked Keith W.S.

"No, why?"

"Well, we must find out where Mr X bought them."

The Black Hand Gang spent the whole afternoon looking for a shop that sold Don Carlos cigars, but without luck. The following day they kept looking. Ralph even examined the stub that their teacher, Mr Smith, had thrown out of the classroom window. Suddenly they heard Frank's trumpet which he used to signal the Gang. The Black Hand Gang crowded round him and Frank whispered softly: "I've found out where you can buy Don Carlos."

 Which shop sold Don Carlos cigars?

---

extraordinary	– außergewöhnlich	occasion	– Gelegenheit
stub	– Stummel	millinary	– Modistin, Hut-
to examine	– untersuchen		macherin
brand	– Sorte	sole supplier	– Alleinlieferant

7 | The Shop Window

"Don Carlos – sole supplier Otto Proud" was the advertisement Frank had seen on a passing van.

That afternoon the Black Hand Gang sat down in the Airport with a telephone directory to look up the address. There were an incredible number of Prouds listed, even a Eulalia Proud, painter of fine porcelain.

"Here it is," exclaimed Frank. "Otto Proud, tobacconist, 12 Frederick Street."

"Let's go," said Ralph.

"Wait a minute." Angela shook her head. "What are we going to do when we get there?"

"Look for a clue," said Frank.

"Yes, but what sort of clue?" Angela asked. "We already know that Mr X smokes Don Carlos. Is there anything special about that? Probably lots of people smoke them."

"Well, we know that Mr X also likes stamps."

"Yes, and …?" said Angela.

"Perhaps Otto Proud is interested in stamps."

Half an hour later they all stood outside Otto Proud's shop. Hundreds of different brands of cigar were in his window, but there were no stamps.

"Just a second," said Keith W.S. "Look, there's a stamp!"

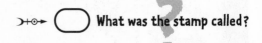 **What was the stamp called?**

advertisement	– Anzeige, Reklame	in stock	– vorrätig
directory	– Telefonbuch	item	– Stück, Exemplar
incredible	– unglaublich		

23

8 | The Forged Zanzibar

The solitary 50 Rupee Zanzibar puzzled the Black Hand Gang for a long time. "Why has Otto Proud only one stamp for sale?" Ralph wondered. "Perhaps he bought up a whole batch cheaply? What do you think?"

But at lunchtime next day Angela raced into the Airport.

"Look, it's impossible!"

"What is?" asked Frank.

"For anyone to have lots of 50 Rupee Zanzibars. They're rare."

"Who says so?"

"My father. His hobby is stamp-collecting and he's an expert."

"She's right," said Ralph, who had just come in, waving a newspaper. "Here, read this." The Black Hand Gang read: "Stamp forgers operating in Newtown."

Seconds later the Gang stood outside Mr X's house. Smoke was coming out of the chimney and they noticed fragments of paper whirling about in the air. Keith W.S. picked up one of the bits. It was singed, but it was clearly a 50 Rupee Zanzibar.

"Just a minute," said Angela, pulling a catalogue out of her bag. "There's a photograph of it in here."

Keith W.S. compared it to the singed stamp.

"Ours is different. It's a forgery," Ralph exclaimed.

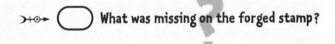 **What was missing on the forged stamp?**

to forge	– fälschen	rare	– selten
forger, forgery	– Fälscher, Fälschung	to operate	– am Werk sein
batch	– Menge, Haufen, Stoß	to whirl	– wirbeln
		to singe	– versengen

Genuine

Forgery

25

9 | Escape by Canal

"But if the flag's missing, he can't sell it," said Frank.

"Of course he can't." Angela replied. "That's why he's burning them. They're imperfect copies. He'll keep the perfect ones and try to get away."

"We must stop him," said Ralph.

The Black Hand Gang took up their posts all round the house and watched the exits. The minutes went slowly by, but nothing happened.

Suddenly there was a trumpet fanfare. Angela, Ralph and Keith W.S. rushed to the bridge.

"He's off," shouted Frank. "He came out of the cellar with a metal case and ran off down the canal bank."

Angela thought quickly. "He's planning to escape abroad," she said. "Let's go to the harbour."

As the Black Hand Gang raced towards the harbour they saw the man with the metal case running down the steps to the jetty. They sprang after him, but arrived too late. The jetty was deserted and so was the little kiosk. Mr X had disappeared.

"Perhaps he's dived under water," Ralph suggested.

"If he had, we'd see his hat floating," said Keith W.S., smiling. "I think he's hidden quite near here."

 **Where had Mr X hidden?**

escape	– Entkommen, Flucht	to race	– rasen, rennen
imperfect	– unvollkommen, schlecht	jetty	– Landungsbrücke, -steg
metal case	– Metallkoffer	deserted	– verlassen
harbour	– Hafen	to float	– treiben

Trapped

Keith W.S. knew in which boat Mr X, the forger, had hidden, because it lay lower in the water than the others. His friends realized it too, but not until Mr X cut through the mooring lines and sped off.

Frank blew another fanfare, "Tallyho", on his trumpet and they gave chase. They ran along the harbour wall and over the bridge to the other side of the canal. Mr X had left his boat and was disappearing at top speed round the corner. Ralph saw him dash into a building site on Bridge Street and then he vanished again.

The Black Hand Gang climbed up a heap of sand.

"Even if we've lost him, we can give the police his description," said Keith W.S.

"That's something, at least," Angela agreed. "Check trousers, black jacket, striped tie ..." She gasped, then whispered urgently, "Ralph, dash off to the phone box and call the police – Emergency, 999."

"999," Ralph repeated. "Tell them to send three cars!" "All right, but why?"

"Because we've got Mr X in a trap. Hurry up!"

>+⊙► ⬭ **How did Angela know where Mr X was hiding?**

to trap	– fangen, eine Falle stellen	building site	– Baustelle
to realize	– bemerken, wahrnehmen	to vanish	– verschwinden
to speed	– eilen	tie	– Schlips
to give chase	– nachjagen, verfolgen	to gasp	– keuchen, nach Luft schnappen
to dash	– flitzen, rasen	emergency	– Notfall

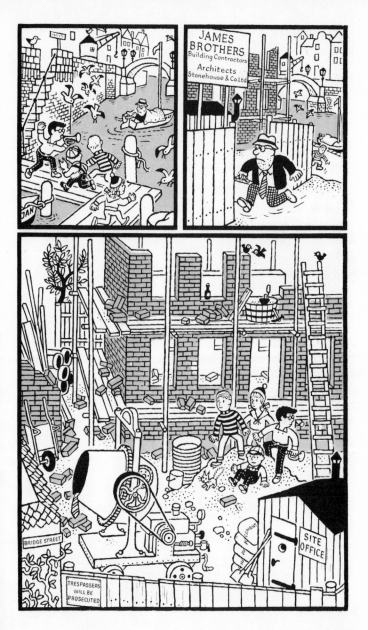

29

Bellyflop

If the police sirens hadn't made such a row, the forger would probably have stayed hidden in the cement mixer. As it was though, the Black Hand Gang saw the striped tie, and Mr X, still holding his metal case, jump from the mixer and disappear head first over the wall.

"He'll kill himself!" Angela exclaimed.

But Mr X didn't hurt himself at all. He made a belly landing in a manure heap.

"What a stink," said Sergeant Shorthouse, as the three cars stopped screeching in the farmyard. They arrested Mr X despite his protests.

"It's not against the law to smell of manure. If I want to, that's my business. Release me at once."

"You are a forger. Where are the stamps you've printed? Show us where they're hidden."

The man said nothing. The police searched the whole area without success. They were just about to let their prisoner go when the Black Hand Gang jumped down from the wall.

"Who are you?" asked Sergeant Shorthouse angrily.

"We are the Black Hand Gang," Frank said, politely. "May we show you where he's hidden the metal case with the forged stamps?"

>─◦─► ◯ **Where did Frank think the case was hidden?**

bellyflop	– Bauchlandung	screech	– quietschen
row	– Lärm	despite	– trotz
as it was though	– so jedoch	to release	– freilassen
manure heap	– Misthaufen	prisoner	– Gefangener

31

12 | The Deep Secret

Mr X had turned pale and not even his many freckles could conceal this.

"Now, where's that case?" Sergeant Shorthouse asked.

Ralph pointed towards the well. "Unless I'm very much mistaken the hook had been up before we came here!"

When the Black Hand Gang rushed to the well the hens scattered in all directions. Sergeant Shorthouse followed, and they all bent over the edge to have a look inside.

The Sergeant asked: "Do you see anything?" The answer was signalled immediately by Frank's trumpet: short short long, which meant: everything o.k., the case is solved. And the echo came back from the well like the thunder of a jet plane.

"You made a good job of it," Sergeant Shorthouse said winking when Ralph took the case from the hook after thirty-seven turns of the handle. Mr X looked away bored to the pigshed while the case was opened and a pile of lilac stamps appeared.

"The 50 Rupee Zanzibar!" the Gang shouted as one man.

"And all of them forged!" Keith W.S. added grinning.

"That remains to be checked!" the Sergeant replied sternly, putting handcuffs on Mr X. And turning again to the Black Hand Gang he said: "I hope you can come and see me at the police station this afternoon.

There are some more details to talk about."

freckles	– Sommersprossen	to make a good job of	– gute Arbeit leisten
to conceal	– verheimlichen		
well	– Brunnen	to wink	– zwinkern
unless I'm mistaken	– wenn ich mich nicht irre	to be bored	– gelangweilt sein
		that remains to be checked	– das muss noch geprüft werden

The Smugglers' Tunnel

I | It Happened at Four Minutes Past Five

One day Ralph burst into the Airport waving a letter. He read it out: "Dear Ralph, I read all about your adventures in the newspaper and how your 'Black Hand Gang' helped the police to catch a thief.

My congratulations to you and your friends.

Your loving uncle, Paul

P.S. Why don't you all come up to my farm in the mountains for a holiday?"

The Black Hand Gang were delighted and, a fortnight later, on the Saturday, they took the train to Green Willow.

"This journey seems to take forever," grumbled Keith W.S.

Ralph looked at his watch: "It's 5.04 p.m. already."

As the train rattled into a tunnel and their compartment was plunged into total darkness, a woman's voice suddenly cried out: "Ow! My foot! Watch where you are treading!"

A door creaked as it opened, letting in an acrid smell of smoke. Then it slammed shut again.

"Who was that at the door?" whispered Frank.

As soon as they came back into daylight Angela murmured: "I know who it was."

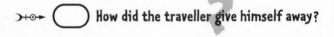 **How did the traveller give himself away?**

congratulation	– Glückwunsch	to tread	– (hin)treten
fortnight	= two weeks	acrid	– scharf
forever	– ewig	it slammed shut	– sie knallte zu
compartment	– Abteil	to give oneself away	– sich verraten
watch!	– hier: passen Sie doch auf		

34

2 | The Mysterious Suitcase

The Black Hand Gang watched the man suspiciously, for he was holding his newspaper upside down. Presently Keith W.S. pulled Frank's sleeve.

"Look! A suitcase!" he whispered, rolling his eyes upwards at the luggage rack above the man's head. "When we went into the tunnel there wasn't one there."

As the train drew into Green Willow station the strange traveller got out first, quickly followed by the Black Hand Gang.

"Hallo, children," came a shout and a man waved his hat. It was Ralph's uncle, Paul Boller. But the Gang slipped past him following their suspect who had left the station.

"See what the number is on his case," Frank ordered.

Only then did they say hello to Uncle Paul and to Fred, the driver of the pony-trap.

"Get in, all of you," called Uncle Paul.

But the Black Hand Gang were still watching the traveller who had now climbed into his car.

"What about the case?" asked Ralph.

"In the boot?" Angela suggested.

But Keith W.S. pinched her arm and winked.

"Don't worry. I know where the case is."

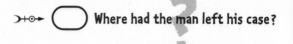 **Where had the man left his case?**

suspiciously	– argwöhnisch	boot	– Kofferraum
sleeve	– Ärmel	to pinch	– kneifen
rack	– Ablage	to wink	– zwinkern
trap	– hier: Einspänner		

3 | The Peephole

Ralph was very puzzled about the case, now safely hidden in the trap under Fred's seat, and he worried about it all evening. As the church clock struck ten, a sound of footsteps outside made him sit up in bed. "Wake up!" he hissed.

The others sat up too. "What's the matter," said Angela, yawning. "It's Fred, with the case!" They were all immediately wide awake.

"Put your socks on," Frank ordered.

They all crept out and into the loft. They hadn't gone far when Ralph held up a warning hand. "There's a light there."

Light was shining up through a knothole in the floor. Ralph tiptoed forward, holding his breath. He could see directly into Fred's room. Fred had just opened the suitcase and was taking out a round tin. With his pocket knife he opened it, shook the contents out onto the table and began to count them.

"Does anyone know what those things are?" Ralph asked.

They each looked in turn through the knothole, Angela last. She got to her feet, clutched her forehead and groaned.

"You'll never believe it! Do you know what he's counting?"

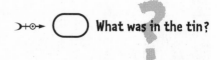

What was in the tin?

to hiss	– zischen	contents	– Inhalt
loft	– Dachboden	in turn	– abwechselnd
wide awake	– hellwach	to clutch the	– sich an die Stirn
knothole	– Astloch	forehead	fassen
to tiptoe	– auf den Zehen-	to groan	– stöhnen
	spitzen gehen		

4 | The Key

Printed clearly on the tin lid were the words "Stock Cubes".

"I'm not convinced," said Ralph when they were back in bed. "We must keep him under observation." And so they did.

But apart from sucking an occasional raw egg in the henhouse he did nothing suspicious. But one evening, while they were collecting glow-worms in the garden, they saw him set off towards the village.

"Come on, after him," said Frank.

They shadowed Fred as far as a pub called *The Blue Knight*.

"I can hear music," said Keith W.S., pointing to a window.

They all crowded round and Keith W.S. pressed his nose to the pane.

"It's very smoky inside," he whispered. Then he gave a startled cry. "There's Fred, he's with a man who's giving him money. Fred's handed over a little key."

"A key," said Angela, puzzled. "Why a key?"

Keith W.S. watched quietly for a while, then he said: "It's very strange – putting stock cubes in a secret cupboard. You'll never guess where the cupboard is."

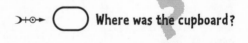 **Where was the cupboard?**

stock cubes	– Brühwürfel	raw	– roh
lid	– Deckel	to set off	– aufbrechen
to be convinced	– überzeugt sein	to shadow	– beschatten
observation	– Beobachtung	pub	– Kneipe
apart from	– außer	to crowd	– sich drängen
to suck	– (leer) saugen	to give a	– voller Über-
occasional	– gelegentlich; hier:	startled cry	raschung
	das eine oder		ausrufen
	andere		

5 | Seek and Find

"Well," said Angela, "one thing is clear enough. The stock cubes are hidden in the secret door of the painting."

"But why all that?" asked Frank thoughtfully.

Next morning they all went back to the pub.

"Should we just go in?" Frank asked.

But Keith W.S. had spotted something interesting among the refuse and held it up triumphantly. It was a small cube. Angela unwrapped it and sniffed it.

"It doesn't smell of anything." She licked it. "Ugh! Bitter," she exclaimed, spitting it out.

Half an hour later the Black Hand Gang were standing in the chemist's shop waiting hopefully for Mr Hancock to examine the stock cube. Suddenly he gasped: "Good heavens!" and took out a reference book.

"Can you tell us what it is?" Angela asked politely.

"Tell you!" snapped Mr Hancock. "This is nothing to do with you. This is a matter for the police." He went to the telephone, but Ralph whispered: "Come on, let's go. I know what's in those cubes."

>+o+ ◯ **What was the substance in the cubes?**

words to the picture:		to unwrap	– auspacken
upset stomach	– Magenschmerzen	to sniff	– an etwas riechen
wart	– Warze	to lick	– an etwas lecken
prescriptions	– Rezepte	to spit	– spucken
narcotics	– Betäubungsmittel	chemist	– Apotheker
ointment	– Salbe	Good heavens!	– Donnerwetter!
		reference book	– Nachschlagewerk, Fachbuch
words to the text:			
thoughtfully	– nachdenklich	polite (-ly)	– höflich
to spot	– erblicken, finden	to snap	– fauchen, bissig
refuse	– Abfall, Kehricht		antworten

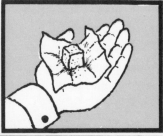

43

6 | What the Postman Brought

The stock cubes were full of drugs, as the Gang had suspected.
"Now I begin to understand!" said Angela. "That queer business with the suitcase and all Fred's coming and going. It's drug smuggling!"

"What shall we do now?" Ralph asked.

"Wait and see," suggested Frank.

The Gang were very busy helping Ralph's uncle on the farm, but they still kept their eyes open. One afternoon a boy arrived. "What do you want?" asked Keith W. S.

"I'm looking for Fred. I have a letter that I have to deliver to him personally." The Black Hand Gang were immediately on the alert. When the boy had handed the letter over, Fred put down his barrow and went quickly to his room. Watching through the window, the Gang saw him tear open the letter.

"Look," muttered Keith W. S. Fred had torn the letter into little pieces which he threw out of the window.

It took the Gang ten minutes to gather up the bits and piece them together in a quiet corner. Then followed a long silence.

"I've got it!" Frank exclaimed. "This is an important message. We shall have plenty to do now."

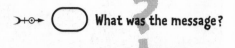 What was the message?

words to the picture:		to deliver	– überbringen, übergeben
cable car	– Drahtseilbahn		
Chief	– Chef	to be on the alert	– hellwach sein
		barrow	– Schubkarre
words to the text:		to tear open	– aufreißen
drug	– Droge	to mutter	– murmeln
queer	– seltsam, sonderlich, komisch	to gather up	– aufsammeln
		to piece together	– zusammensetzen

NDE
BLE

HIE

RE
CA

ZVOUS
CAR

AY
OURS

F.

C

ND
oo H

SU
14.

45

7 | The Meeting

"Rendezvous cable car Sunday 2.00 p.m. Chief," was the text of the message. The Black Hand Gang were on time at the meeting-place. Fred was the first to arrive, with the suitcase, and he was soon joined by the man from the train. They waited near the café. A few minutes later the cable car swept into the hall and the passengers streamed out. "Look!" Frank whispered. A stranger had approached the other two. He nodded to them and they all went to sit down in the café to have a beer. They looked round cautiously before they began to speak.

Behind the hedge, however, crouched the Black Hand Gang, listening as hard as they could.

Keith W.S. muttered softly: "I can't catch what they're saying."

"Shhhh!" whispered Angela. She repeated: "5.10 p.m. – 5.10 p.m.?"

"What's happening at 5.10 p.m.?" Frank asked when the men had finished their beer and left.

"It's something to do with the trains. They're planning to deliver something. Presumably in the tunnel."

"But when?" said Ralph impatiently.

Angela shrugged. "I couldn't hear."

"But I do," said Keith W.S.. "There's only one day it can be."

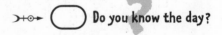 ⊶► ◯ **Do you know the day?**

words to the text:		to catch	– hier: verstehen
to join	– sich anschließen, dazugesellen	presumably	– vermutlich
		words to the picture:	
to sweep	– hier: schweben	to depart	– (ab)fahren
to approach	– sich nähern	local train	– am Ort haltender
to crouch	– hocken, ducken		Zug, Vorortzug

47

8 | A Dark Passageway

Only on Saturday was there a 5.10 p.m. train arriving at Green Willow. Keith W.S. had read the timetable.

"What happens next?" Ralph asked.

"We must go to the tunnel," Frank said.

So on Saturday afternoon the Black Hand Gang were walking towards the tunnel. Its entrance was very close to the border.

"Keep close to the side as you go," Frank ordered.

Inside the tunnel it grew darker and darker until Angela had to switch on her torch. When they had reached the middle of the tunnel, she suddenly stopped.

"Shhh! Can you hear?"

"It sounds like water," said Keith W.S. "Shine your torch over there."

The torch beam played over the opposite wall, illuminating an opening in the rock. The Black Hand Gang stepped across the rails. Keith W.S. bent down and exclaimed in surprise. "A cave, what a find! Do you think the smugglers use this as a route to the railway tunnel?"

"Don't be silly," Angela said. "No one has come through here in years."

"Oh, yes, someone has," Frank answered. "Look there!"

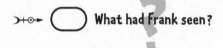 **What had Frank seen?**

border	– Grenze	opening	– Öffnung
torch	– Taschenlampe	rail	– Schiene
beam	– Strahl	cave	– Höhle
to illuminate	– erhellen, beleuchten		

49

9 | A Man is Missing

The candle stump showed that someone *had* been in the tunnel.
Angela said: "It must be smugglers."

"How do they get in?" asked Ralph.

"No idea," answered Frank, "but I'm sure, the border is some-
where right in the middle of the cave. Do you suppose the
smugglers …"

"Shhh!" hissed Keith W. S.

They all listened.

"Voices," said Ralph, after a few moments.

They all crept further along the passage. The sound of voices
grew clearer and now they could see a faint light on the damp
walls. The passage opened to a vast cave with electric light in it.

"Stalactites," Angela whispered. "I bet the entrance is on the
other side of the border."

They could now see the group of tourists and the guide whose
voices they had heard. The children watched closely as the
group was led around. But when it stopped in front of a stalac-
tite called the "witch's nose", Ralph whispered in surprise:
"One of them is missing."

Angela looked at the group again. "You're right and I remem-
ber what he had in his hand."

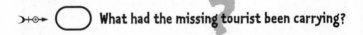 **What had the missing tourist been carrying?**

candle stump	– Kerzenstummel	stalactite	– hängender Tropf-stein
further	– weiter		
faint	– schwach	to bet	– wetten
damp	– feucht	witch	– Hexe
vast	– riesig, weit		

10

The Train

"The missing man was carrying a suitcase," said Angela.

"Quick, let's go back to the tunnel," Frank said.

They hurried back down the dark passage. It was not long before they heard a distant rumbling.

"It's the train," said Keith W.S., looking at his watch. "It's 5.04 p.m.. This must be the smugglers' train."

The rumbling came nearer and nearer, and as they crawled out into the tunnel, the train came thundering towards them.

They saw the man with the suitcase jump on.

"Duck!" shouted Frank, as the train went by.

But the man didn't jump off.

"He's seen us," Angela shouted. "Let's follow him."

The Black Hand Gang ran the short distance to Green Willow and sprinted breathlessly into the station just in time to see the man get on his car and take off at top speed. The Black Hand Gang chased after him along Station Street until they came to a crossroads.

"It's hopeless," said Ralph.

"No," said Angela, "wait a minute. They took that street."

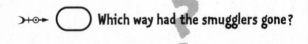 **Which way had the smugglers gone?**

to rumble	– poltern, rumpeln	to take off	– starten, abfahren
to thunder	– donnern	crossroads	– Kreuzung

53

11

Dark Deeds

Angela had noticed a skid mark on the street leading to the market place. When the Black Hand Gang arrived there, however, there was no sign of the car.

"I expect they've gone to find Fred," suggested Keith W. S.

"What are we waiting for then?" asked Frank.

It was dusk when they reached Uncle Paul's farm. Keith W. S. stopped.

"Look, I can see a ghost."

Fred was slinking along by the wall of the house. He went into the tractor shed and the Black Hand Gang followed him.

"Hush!" said Angela softly. She had seen the smugglers' car.

"Keep your heads down or they'll see us," Frank ordered.

They all ducked down. A faint murmur of voices and clatter of tools was all they could hear. After a while there was a silence. They peered out cautiously. The car was still there and they could see nothing suspicious.

Suddenly Ralph caught his breath: "What a nerve! I know what they've been doing."

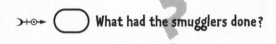 What had the smugglers done?

deeds	– Taten, Machenschaften	to slink	– schleichen
skid mark	– Rutschspur	clatter	– Klappern
dusk	– Abenddämmerung	nerve	– hier: Frechheit

55

12

A Gentleman

When the Black Hand Gang noticed that the number plates had been exchanged, they decided they ought to tell Uncle Paul about it. "Let's go and find him," said Ralph.

Mr Boller was in the living room doing the books. When the children told him about the smugglers he burst out laughing.

"What a story! Fred's not a criminal. I can't believe it. Let's go and talk to him."

"Supposing he's armed?" asked Angela hesitantly.

"There are no firearms on my farm. In fact, there isn't so much as a firework." Uncle Paul, still laughing, led the way to Fred's room. He knocked, and would have opened the door but it was locked. The key turned on the inside and the door opened. There stood Fred, dressed in his best clothes.

"Hello," said Uncle Paul. "Where are you off to?"

"I – I – I'm going to the cinema," he replied awkwardly.

"Well, we won't bother you now. It was all a lot of nonsense anyway," said Uncle Paul cheerfully.

But Ralph pulled his sleeve and whispered something to him. Mr. Boller started, gave a low whistle and said sternly. "That's a different matter."

>+◦+ ◯ **What did Ralph point out to Mr Boller?**

to exchange	– austauschen, aus- wechseln	to be off to	– (etwas) vorhaben
books	– hier: Rechnungs- bücher	awkwardly	– verlegen, unge- schickt
criminal	– Krimineller	to bother	– belästigen, stören
supposing	– angenommen	to start	– hier: stutzen
armed	– bewaffnet	sternly	– streng
firearms	– (Feuer-)Waffen	matter	– Angelegenheit

13 | Send for Habel

Ralph had noticed the gun hidden in the bed. Mr Boller sighed as he left the room with the children. Then he said softly, "Go and fetch the police. Tell Constable Habel the whole story. Get him to come quickly while I keep an eye on Fred."

"Can't we phone him?" asked Angela.

"We'd better not. Fred might hear. His room is next door to the living room."

The Gang stole out of the house and as they went they saw Fred watching them through the window.

"Run for it!" shouted Frank.

In two minutes they had reached the police station. Constable Habel did not waste any time. He pulled on his jacket, picked up his gun and bundled the Black Hand Gang into his car.

When they reached the farmyard they all jumped out.

"He's still inside," whispered Uncle Paul, who had been keeping watch outside the door.

"Let's have him out here, then," said Constable Habel, taking out his gun.

"Oh, no!" cried Frank: "We're too late. He's escaped."

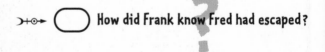 **How did Frank know Fred had escaped?**

to sigh	– seufzen	to bundle	– hier: verfrachten
to steal out	– sich hinausstehlen	to escape	– flüchten
to waste	– versäumen, vergeuden		

58

59

14 | By the Milestone

Frank was right. Fred had climbed through the window, over-turning the flowerpot as he jumped. The Constable and the Gang ran across to the tractor shed, but the car had gone.

"What sort of car?" snapped the Constable.

As Keith W.S. was about to tell him, Angela interrupted.

"Come here a minute, Constable."

"What's the matter?"

"I've found this," she said, giving him a scrap of paper.

"This is bad news," he muttered. "This comes from a cartridge wrapper."

The Constable acted quickly, telephoning round all the other police stations in the district. Then he ordered the Black Hand Gang back into the car and roared off towards Newtown. They had gone about thirty miles before he stopped and said: "There's no point in going on. They must have taken another road. Climb out while I turn the car."

The Black Hand Gang climbed out and watched to see that the car didn't back into a ditch. Suddenly Angela cried, "Stop!"

Constable Habel braked sharply and called, "What's the matter?"

"This *is* the right road. The smugglers *did* come this way."

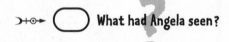 **What had Angela seen?**

to overturn	– umwerfen	to roar off	– abzischen, los-donnern
shed	– Schuppen		
scrap	– Fetzen, Stück	to back	= to go back
cartridge wrapper	– Patronenschachtel	ditch	– Graben
		to brake	– bremsen

61

| # Roadblock

The Constable inspected the box of cartridges that Angela had found. "This is the box, from which that scrap of paper came," he said.

They all got back into the car and set off again.

"If we can't catch them before they reach the bridge, we'll have lost them."

A few minutes later they saw the blinking of a red light. Constable Habel stopped sharply.

The Black Hand Gang jumped out and Frank cried: "What luck. It's another police car."

The policeman, somewhat surprised, asked: "Where have you come from?"

"We're chasing the smugglers."

"We've caught them," he said. "They tried to run me down, but we had scattered nails right across the road. All the tyres burst and we arrested these two men here."

The children recognized them at once.

"And a third man escaped."

"Fred!"

The Black Hand Gang climbed down the river bank.

"Look!" said Keith W. S. "There's our friend."

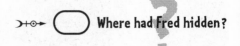 **Where had Fred hidden?**

roadblock	– Straßensperre	to scatter	– verstreuen
to chase	– verfolgen	nail	– Nagel
to run down	– über den Haufen fahren	tyre	– Reifen
		bank	– Ufer

63

16

The Old Coach House

Keith W.S. had spotted Fred clinging to the girders, and they ran down to the river's edge, closely followed by Constable Habel and the policeman. "Come down!" he shouted.

Fred did not answer.

"I'll give you three seconds!" The Constable had counted to two when Fred jumped into the water.

"He's swimming away!" Angela cried.

"Come on," said the Constable. "The water is not deep here. We must cross the bridge and cut him off."

The Black Hand Gang crossed to the other side, and pushed their way through the bushes. There was no sign of Fred.

"What shall we do now?" Ralph asked.

The Constable scratched his chin. "I think we'd better send for reinforcements. There are too few of us."

But Frank pointed to a building from whose windows shone a flickering light. "Could he be in there?"

"That's an inn called *The Old Coach House*," said the policeman. "It's a very rough place. We'd better take a look."

They peered through the window.

"There you are," said Frank, "There's slippery Fred. Can't you see him, Constable?"

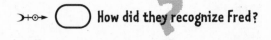 How did they recognize Fred?

to spot	– entdecken	to flicker	– flackern
to cling	– sich festhalten, klammern	rough place	– hier: üble Kneipe
girder	– Verstrebung	slippery	– a) gerissen; b) rutschig, schlüpfrig
to scratch	– kratzen		
reinforcement	– Verstärkung		

17 | A Shot

"Good lad!" exclaimed the Constable when Frank pointed out the man's soaking trousers. "We'll get him this time." The Constable opened the door of *The Old Coach House*.

The Black Hand Gang followed him. Fred must have noticed the sudden draught, for his hand leapt to his pistol. He fired. There was a tinkle of glass and the room was plunged into darkness.

"He's escaped again!" The Constable's angry voice made itself heard in the darkness. The silence was broken by the slamming of a door.

"There's a door on the left," called Angela.

Someone at the bar struck a match and the Constable saw the door for himself. Pistol in hand, he rushed through it, followed by his companions.

A short passage led them into a private room. Keith W. S. put the light on.

"He's vanished," said the policeman.

"The window!" exclaimed Angela. "But he'll be back soon."

"How do you know that?"

Ralph answered: "Angela's right. Fred's left the suitcase behind."

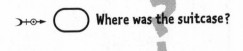 **Where was the suitcase?**

---

lad	= boy	tinkle	– Klirren
draught	– Luftzug	to plunge	– tauchen
to leap to	– hier: blitzschnell packen	slamming	– Knallen

67

18 | Beware of the Dog

Constable Habel heaved the suitcase out of the piano and opened it. It was full of stock cubes. He shook his head. "These are supposed to be full of drugs?"

Frank said, "Have a taste."

The Constable tasted one and shuddered. They had to use all their strength to get the suitcase shut again. Then he said: "I'm very grateful to you all. Let's go back to the car and fetch help. We shall need all we can get if we're going to catch Fred."

He took the case and started towards the door. At that moment a dog started a frantic barking. The Black Hand Gang rushed to the back door and into the yard.

"Call the landlord!" cried Angela.

Keith W.S. ran to fetch him.

"That's my dog," said the landlord, turning on the outside light.

They saw the dog scrabbling away at the trunk of an apple tree. Fred, his trousers in shreds, was clinging to the branches.

"Take care!" shouted the policeman. "He's armed."

But Ralph only laughed. "Don't worry. He's dropped his gun, and he's scared to death."

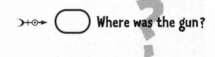 **Where was the gun?**

Beware of the dog	– Vorsicht, bissiger Hund!	to scrabble	– scharren
to heave	– heben	shred	– Fetzen
strength	– Kraft	take care!	– Vorsicht!
frantic	– wütend, rasend	scared to death	– zu Tode erschrocken
landlord	– Wirt		

The End of a Chase

After Sergeant Habel had seized the pistol, which Fred had thrown among the bottles, he put handcuffs on Fred and took him away into custody.

Three days later the children's holidays came to an end.

"I hope you'll soon come again," Mr Boller shouted when the train started moving out of the station. He stood waving his hat until the train had disappeared into the dark tunnel the secret of which the Black Hand Gang had solved.

How many correct answers did you score? Here is a guide to your detective ability:

● **1–10 correct answers:**

Never mind. No man is born a master.

● **11–20 correct answers:**

You have a very observant eye. If you train yourself to notice things (at home, at school and outside) you should be able to develop them still further.

● **21–29 correct answers:**

You definitely have a sharp eye and one day you will certainly reach the standards of Sherlock Holmes. But don't forget that he, too, didn't stop learning throughout his life. So don't look upon doing your homework as a waste of time.

to seize	– hier: beschlag-nahmen	to have a very observant eye	– eine gute Beobach-tungsgabe haben
handcuffs	– Handschellen	definitely	– zweifellos
to put into custody	– verhaften	throughout his life	– sein ganzes Leben hindurch
to score	– zusammenbekom-men, anrechnen	to look upon as	– betrachten als
no man is born a master	– es ist noch kein Meister vom Himmel gefallen		

Vocabulary

ability [ə'bɪlɪtɪ] – Fähigkeit
acrid ['ækrɪd] – scharf
advertisement [əd'vɜːtɪsment] – Anzeige, Reklame
(to be on the) alert [ə'lɜːt] – hellwach sein
apart from [ə'pɑːt] – außer
to approach [ə'prəʊtʃ] – sich nähern
armed [ɑːmd] – bewaffnet
artificial [ɑːtɪ'fɪʃl] – künstlich
awkwardly ['ɔːkwədlɪ] – verlegen, ungeschickt

bank [bæŋk] – Ufer
barrow ['bærəʊ] – Schubkarre
batch [bætʃ] – Menge, Haufen, Stoß
beam [biːm] – Strahl
bellyflop ['belɪflɒp] – Bauchlandung
to be off to [biː'ɔːf] – etwas vorhaben
to bet [bet] – wetten
beware of [bɪ'weə] – Vorsicht
books [bʊks] – hier: Rechnungsbücher
boot [buːt] – Kofferraum
border ['bɔːdə] – Grenze
to be bored [bɔːd] – gelangweilt sein
to bother ['bɒðə] – belästigen, stören
to brake [breɪk] – bremsen
brand [brænd] – Sorte
building site [bɪldɪŋ saɪt] – Baustelle
to bundle [bʌndl] – hier: verfrachten

71

⌒‑⊙‑→

(C)

cable car ['keɪbl'kɑː]	– Drahtseilbahn
to camouflage ['kæmʊflɑːʒ]	– tarnen
candle stump ['kændl'stʌmp]	– Kerzenstummel
(to take) care [keə]	– Vorsicht
cartridge wrapper ['kɑːtrɪdʒ'ræpə]	– Patronenschachtel
to catch [[kætʃ]	– fangen
cautiously ['kɔːʃəslɪ]	– vorsichtig
cave [keɪv]	– Höhle
(to give) chase [tʃeɪs]	– nachjagen, verfolgen
to chase	– verfolgen
to check [tʃek]	– überprüfen, auswerten
check trousers ['traʊzəz]	– karierte Hosen
(that remains to be) checked	– das muss noch geprüft werden
chemist ['kemɪst]	– Apotheker
chest [tʃest]	– Truhe
to chew [tʃuː]	– kauen
chief [tʃiːf]	– Chef
clatter ['klætə]	– Klappern
to cling [klɪŋ]	– festhalten, klammern
clue [kluː]	– hier: Spur, Hinweis
compartment [kəm'pɑːtmənt]	– Abteil
to conceal [kən'siːl]	– verheimlichen
congratulation [kəngrætju'leɪʃn]	– Glückwunsch
contents ['kɒntents]	– Inhalt
to be convinced [kən'vɪnst]	– überzeugt sein
to cover ['kʌvə]	– sichern, beobachten
to crack [kræk]	– knacken
to crawl [krɔːl]	– kriechen

creaking [kriːkɪŋ]	– krächzend
creeper [kriːpə]	– Kletterpflanze
criminal ['krɪmɪnl]	– Krimineller
crossroads ['krɒsrəʊdz]	– Kreuzung
to crouch [kraʊtʃ]	– hocken, ducken
to crowd [kraʊd]	– sich drängen
(to put into) custody ['kʌstədɪ]	– verhaften

damp [dæmp]	– feucht
to dash [dæʃ]	– flitzen, rasen
to dawn [dɔːn]	– dämmern
deeds [diːdz]	– Taten, Machenschaften
to deliver [dɪ'lɪvə]	– überbringen, übergeben
to depart [dɪ'pɑːt]	– abfahren
despite [dɪs'paɪt]	– trotz
directory [dɪ'rektərɪ]	– Telefonbuch
disguised [dɪs'gaɪzd]	– verkleidet
ditch [dɪtʃ]	– Graben
draught [drɑːft]	– Luftzug
drug [drʌg]	– Droge
dusk [dʌsk]	– Abenddämmerung

emergency [i'mɜːdʒənsɪ]	– Notfall
to enable [ɪ'neɪbl]	– befähigen, sich in die Lage versetzen
entrance ['entrəns]	– Eingang
to escape [ɪs'keɪp]	– entkommen, Flucht
to examine [ɪg'zæmɪn]	– untersuchen
to exchange [ɪks'tʃeɪndʒ]	– austauschen, auswechseln
extraordinary [ɪks'trɔːdnrɪ]	– außergewöhnlich

73

F

faded [feɪded]	– verblichen
faint [feɪnt]	– schwach
firearms [ˈfaɪəɑːmz]	– Feuer-Waffen
in a flash [flæʃ]	– im Nu
to flicker [ˈflɪkə]	– flackern
to float [fləʊt]	– treiben
forever [fəˈrevə]	– ewig
to forge [fɔːdʒ]	– fälschen
forger [ˈfɔːdʒə]	– Fälscher
forgery [ˈfɔːdʒərɪ]	– Fälschung
fortnight [ˈfɔːtnaɪt]	– 14 Tage (2 Wochen)
frantic [ˈfræntɪk]	– wütend, rasend
freckles [ˈfreklz]	– Sommersprossen
to frown [fraʊn]	– die Stirn runzeln
further [ˈfəːðə]	– weiter

G

gang [gæŋ]	– Bande
to gasp [gɑːsp]	– keuchen, nach Luft schnappen
to gather up [ˈgæðərˈʌp]	– aufsammeln
to get up to some funny tricks	– lustige Einfälle haben
girder [ˈgəːdə]	– Verstrebung
to give a startled cry [stɑːtld kraɪ]	– voller Überraschung ausrufen
to give oneself away	– sich verraten
gnome [nəʊm]	– Zwerg
to give chase [tʃeɪs]	– nachjagen, verfolgen
to groan [grəʊn]	– stöhnen
(be on) guard [gɑːd]	– auf der Lauer sein

H

handcuffs [ˈhændkʌfs]	– Handschellen
handprint [ˈhændprɪnt]	– Handabdruck

harbour [ˈhɑːbə]	– Hafen
to heave [hiːv]	– heben
(good) heavens! [gʊdˈhevnz]	– Donnerwetter!
heel [hɪːl]	– Absatz
to hiss [hɪs]	– zischen

←⊙–C
(I)

to illuminate [ɪˈljuːmɪneɪt]	– erhellen, beleuchten
imperfect [ɪmˈpɜːfɪkt]	– unvollkommen, schlecht
incredible [ɪnˈkredɪbl]	– unglaublich
inseparable [ɪnːsepərəbl]	– unzertrennlich
intently [ɪnˈtentlɪ]	– gespannt
item [ˈaɪtəm]	– Stück, Exemplar

←⊙–C
(J)

jetty [ˈdʒetɪ]	– Landungsbrücke, Landungssteg
to join [dʒɔɪn]	– sich anschließen, dazugesellen

←⊙–C
(K)

keep a constant watch [ˈkɒnstənt wɒtʃ]	– ständig beobachten
kids = children [kɪdz]	– Kinder
knothole [ˈnɒthəʊl]	– Astloch

←⊙–C
(L)

landlord [ˈlænlɔːd]	– Wirt
leader [ˈliːdə]	– Anführer
to leap [liːp]	– hier: blitzschnell packen
to lick [lɪk]	– an etwas lecken
lid [lɪd]	– Deckel
local train [ˈləʊkəl ˈtreɪn]	– Vorortzug
to look upon as	– betrachten als

(M)

to make a good job of it	– gute Arbeit leisten
manure heap [mə'njʊə hiːp]	– Misthaufen
matter ['mætə]	– Angelegenheit
message ['mesɪdʒ]	– Botschaft
metal case ['metl'keɪs]	– Metallkoffer
millinary ['mɪlɪnərɪ]	– Modistin, Hutmacherin
minutely [maɪ'njuːtlɪ]	– peinlich genau
to moor [mʊə]	– festmachen
to mutter ['mʌtə]	– murmeln

(N)

nail [neɪl]	– Nagel
narcotics [nɑːˈkɒtɪks]	– Betäubungsmittel
nerve [nəːv]	– hier: Frechheit
nettles ['netlz]	– Nesseln

(O)

observation [ɒbzəˈveɪʃn]	– Beobachtung
obvious ['ɒbvɪəs]	– klar, einleuchtend
occasion [əˈkeɪʒən]	– Gelegenheit
ointment ['ɔɪntmənt]	– Salbe
opening ['əʊpnɪŋ]	– Öffnung
to operate ['ɒpəreɪt]	– am Werk sein
to overturn [əʊvəˈtɜːn]	– umwerfen

(P)

patience ['peɪʃns]	– Geduld
to peep [piːp]	– hervorgucken
to piece together [piːs təˈgeðə]	– zusammensetzen
pigeon loft ['pɪdʒɪn lɒft]	– Taubenschlag
to pin to [pɪn]	– anheften an
pinch [pɪntʃ]	– kneifen
to plunge [plʌndʒ]	– tauchen
polite [pəˈlaɪt]	– höflich

76

power of observation   – Beobachtungsgabe
  [ɒbzə'veɪʃn]
prescription [prɪs'krɪptʃn]   – Rezepte
presumably [prɪ'zjuːməblɪ]   – vermutlich
prisoner ['prizənə]   – Gefangener
pub [pʌb]   – Kneipe

queer [kwɪə]   – seltsam, sonderlich, komisch
quick-witted ['kwɪk'wɪtɪd]   – schlagfertig, aufgeweckt

to race [reɪs]   – rennen, rasen
rack [ræk]   – Ablage
rail [reɪl]   – Schiene
to raise [reɪz]   – anheben, hochheben
rare [reə]   – selten
ray of light [reɪəvlaɪt]   – Lichtstrahl
to realize ['rɪəlaɪz]   – bemerken, wahrnehmen
recognize ['rekəgnaɪz]   – (wieder) erkennen
reference book ['refrəns]   – Nachschlagewerk,
  Fachbuch

refuse ['refjuːs]   – Abfall, Kehricht
reinforcement ['riːn'fɔːsmənt]   – Verstärkung
to release [rɪ'liːs]   – frei lassen
to reward [rɪ'wɔːd]   – belohnen
roadblock ['rəʊdblɒk]   – Straßensperre
to roar off ['rɔːr'ɔf]   – abzischen, losdonnern
rough place [rʌf pleɪs]   – hier: üble Kneipe
row [rəʊ]   – Lärm
to rumble ['rʌmbl]   – poltern, rumpeln
to run down [rʌn]   – über den Haufen fahren

S

saunter ['sɔːntə]	– schlendern
scamper ['skæmpə]	– hüpfen, hier: klettern
scared to death [skɛəd]	– zu Tode erschrocken
to scatter ['skætə]	– verstreuen
score [skɔː]	– Punktzahl, Trefferzahl
to score	– zusammenbekommen, anrechnen
to scrabble ['skræbl]	– scharren
scrap [skræp]	– Fetzen, Stück
to scratch [skrætʃ]	– kratzen
to screech [skriːtʃ]	– quietschen
to scribble ['skrɪbl]	– kritzeln
scrub [skrʌb]	– wischen, scheuern
secret ['siːkrɪt]	– Geheimnis
to seize [siːz]	– hier: beschlagnahmen
sergant ['sɑːdʒnt]	– Wachtmeister
to set off [set]	– aufbrechen
to shadow ['ʃædəʊ]	– beschatten
shed [ʃed]	– Schuppen
shred [ʃred]	– Fetzen
skid mark [skɪdmɑːk]	– Rutschspur
it slammed shut [slæmd ʃʌt]	– sie knallte zu
sleuth [sluːθ]	– Detektiv
sleeve [sliːv]	– Ärmel
slippery ['slɪpərɪ]	– gerissen; rutschig, schlüpfrig
snap [snæp]	– Knacken
to sniff [snɪf]	– an etwas riechen
sole supplier [səʊl sə'plaɪə]	– Alleinlieferant
soot [sut]	– Ruß
to speed, sped, sped [spiːd, sped]	– eilen

to spit, spat, spat, [spɪt, spæt]	– spucken
to spot [spɔt]	– erblicken, finden
stalactite ['stæləktaɪt]	– hängender Tropfstein
to stare [steə] at	– anstarren
to start [stɑːt]	– hier: stutzen
startled [stɑːtld]	– erschreckt
to steal out [stiːl]	– sich hinausstehlen
sternly [stəːnlɪ]	– streng
stock cubes [stɔk kjuːbz]	– Brühwürfel
in stock [in stɔk]	– vorrätig
strength [streŋθ]	– Kraft
stub [stʌb]	– Stummel
to suck [sʌk]	– (leer) saugen
supposing [sə'pəʊziŋ]	– angenommen
sure [ʃuə]	– sicher
suspect [səs'pekt]	– Verdächtiger
suspiciously [səs'pɪʃəsli]	– argwöhnisch
to sweep [swiːp]	– kehren, hier: schweben
startled [stɑːtld]	– erschreckt

←⊙–C
(T)

to tail [teɪl]	– beschatten
to take a stroll [teɪka strəʊl]	– einen Streifengang machen
to take off [teɪk ɔf]	– starten, abfahren
to tear open (tore, torn) [teə, tɔː, tɔːn]	– aufreißen
thoroughly ['θʌrəli]	– gründlich
thoughtful ['θɔːtfʊl]	– nachdenklich
throughout his life [θruː'aʊt]	– sein ganzes Leben hindurch
to thunder ['θʌndə]	– donnern
tie [tai]	– Schlips
tinkle ['tiŋkl]	– klirren

to tiptoe ['tɪptəʊ]	– auf Zehenspitzen gehen
tire ['taɪə]	– Reifen
torch [tɔːtʃ]	– Taschenlampe
to track down [træk]	– zur Strecke bringen
trail [treɪl]	– Fährte
to trap [træp]	– fangen, eine Falle stellen
trap	– hier: Einspänner
trap door	– Falltür, Geheimtür
to tread [tred]	– (hin)treten
truth [truːθ]	– Wahrheit
tulip ['tjuːlɪp]	– Tulpe
in turn [tɜːn]	– abwechselnd

U

unless I'm mistaken [ən'les]	– wenn ich mich nicht irre
to unwrap ['ʌn'ræp]	– auspacken
to upset [ʌp'set]	– durcheinander bringen, verwirren
upset stomach [~'stʌmək]	– Magenverstimmung

V

to vanish ['vænɪʃ]	– verschwinden
vast [vɑːst]	– riesig, weit

W

wart [wɔːt]	– Warze
to waste [weɪst]	– versäumen, vergeuden
watch! [wɒtʃ]	– hier: passen Sie doch auf!
(to keep) watch	– ständig beobachten
well [wel]	– Brunnen
to whirl [wɜːl]	– wirbeln
wide awake [waɪdə'weɪk]	– hellwach
to wink [wɪŋk]	– zwinkern
witch [wɪtʃ]	– Hexe